1998
Works for
2026
2037
2043
2054

EDWARD GOREY
The Gashlycrumb Tinies

*An Appalling Alphabet
which introduces a Gallery
of enchanting tots
and produces a Gasp
of involuntary mirth
when they attain their
Dreadful Demises*

1 9 9 8
deluxe
engagement
book

Catalog No. 98004
Published by Pomegranate Calendars & Books,
Box 6099, Rohnert Park, California 94927
© 1997 Edward Gorey

Available in Canada from Firefly Books Ltd.,
3680 Victoria Park Avenue, Willowdale, Ontario M2H 3K1

Available in the U.K. and mainland Europe from Pomegranate Europe Ltd.,
Fullbridge House, Fullbridge, Maldon, Essex CM9 7LE, England

Available in Australia from Boobook Publications Pty. Ltd.,
P.O. Box 163 or Freepost 1, Tea Gardens 2324

Available in New Zealand from Randy Horwood Ltd.,
P.O. Box 32-077, Devonport, Auckland

Available in Asia (including the Middle East), Africa, and Latin America from
Pomegranate International Sales, 113 Babcombe Drive,
Thornhill, Ontario L3T 1M9, Canada

Pomegranate also publishes the works of Edward Gorey in several other
formats. Our full-color catalog showing 170 1998 calendars is available for one
dollar. We offer our other full-color catalogs (illustrating our notecards, boxed
notes, notecard folios, miniprints, postcards, books of postcards, address
books, books of days, posters, art magnets, knowledge cards, bookmarks,
journals, and books) for nominal fees.
For more information on obtaining catalogs and ordering, please write to
Pomegranate, Box 6099, Rohnert Park, California 94927.

Front cover:
H is for Hector done in by a thug

Designed by Harrah Argentine

THIS DELUXE ENGAGEMENT BOOK features the wickedly witty and delightfully detailed drawings of Edward Gorey, author-illustrator of *The Doubtful Guest*, *The Abandoned Sock*, *The Gilded Bat*, *The Curious Sofa*, and numerous other books. Gorey's drawings have been exhibited at the California College of Arts and Crafts, Oakland; the Minnesota Institute of Arts, Minneapolis; the Academic Center, University of Texas, Austin; the San Francisco Public Library; Pennsylvania State University; the Sterling Memorial Library, Yale University; and the Graham Gallery, New York; among other venues. Gorey has designed sets and costumes for a number of plays and stage productions, including the Broadway play *Dracula; Murder*, a David Gordon ballet performed by the American Ballet Theatre at the War Memorial Opera House in San Francisco; *The Mikado*, staged by Carnegie Mellon University; and many local plays in Cape Cod, Massachusetts, where he currently resides. In addition, he is the creator of the animated titles that introduce PBS's *Mystery* series, which first aired in 1980 and is featured on public television stations nationwide.

A is for AMY who fell down the stairs

B is for BASIL assaulted by bears

DECEMBER/JANUARY

monday | 363

29

new moon

tuesday | 364

30

wednesday | 365

31

thursday | 1

1

NEW YEAR'S DAY

friday | 2

2

saturday | 3

3

sunday | 4

NOTES

4

5 | m o n d a y

first quarter

5

6 | t u e s d a y

6

7 | w e d n e s d a y

7

Dr. Hume 11:10

8 | t h u r s d a y

8

9 | f r i d a y

9

10 | s a t u r d a y

10

S	M	T	W	T	F	S
				1	2	3
4	5	6	7	8	9	10
11	12	13	14	15	16	17
18	19	20	21	22	23	24
25	26	27	28	29	30	31

JAN

11 | s u n d a y

11

JANUARY

monday | 12

12
full moon

tuesday | 13

13
Staff — food!

wednesday | 14

14

thursday | 15

MARTIN LUTHER KING JR.'S BIRTHDAY

15

friday | 16

16

saturday | 17

17

sunday | 18

NOTES

18

MARTIN LUTHER KING JR.'S BIRTHDAY (OBSERVED)

19 | **m o n d a y**

19

20 | **t u e s d a y**

last quarter moon

20

Axec C - 4
Legis wkshop - 5:30-7

21 | **w e d n e s d a y**

21

22 | **t h u r s d a y**

22

23 | **f r i d a y**

23

24 | **s a t u r d a y**

24

S	M	T	W	T	F	S	JAN
				1	2	3	
4	5	6	7	8	9	10	
11	12	13	14	15	16	17	
18	19	20	21	22	23	24	
25	26	27	28	29	30	31	

25 | **s u n d a y**

25

C is for CLARA who wasted away

D is for DESMOND thrown out of a sleigh

JANUARY/FEBRUARY

monday | 26

26

tuesday | 27 *Dr. Wagner – 9 am*

27

wednesday | 28

28 *new moon*

thursday | 29

29

friday | 30

30

saturday | 31

31

sunday | 32 | *NOTES*

1

FEBRUARY

Legis Reception – Santa Fe	33 **monday** **2**
	34 **tuesday** *first quarter* **3**
	35 **wednesday** **4**
	36 **thursday** **5**
Dr. W – 11 Am	37 **friday** **6**
	38 **saturday** **7**

S	M	T	W	T	F	S	FEB
1	2	3	4	5	6	7	
8	9	10	11	12	13	14	
15	16	17	18	19	20	21	
22	23	24	25	26	27	28	

39 **sunday** **8**

FEBRUARY

monday | 40
9

tuesday | 41
10
Exec. C.

wednesday | 42
11
full moon

thursday | 43
LINCOLN'S BIRTHDAY
12

friday | 44
13

saturday | 45
VALENTINE'S DAY
14

sunday | 46
NOTES
15

PRESIDENTS' DAY | 47 | m o n d a y

16

8 — Dr. Wagner | 48 | t u e s d a y

17

| 49 | w e d n e s d a y

18

| 50 | t h u r s d a y

last quarter **19**

| 51 | f r i d a y

20

| 52 | s a t u r d a y

21

S	M	T	W	T	F	S
1	2	3	4	5	6	7
8	9	10	11	12	13	14
15	16	17	18	19	20	21
22	23	24	25	26	27	28

FEB | WASHINGTON'S BIRTHDAY | 53 | s u n d a y

22

E is for ERNEST who choked on a peach

F is for FANNY sucked dry by a leech

FEBRUARY/MARCH

monday | 54

23

tuesday | 55

24

wednesday | 56

ASH WEDNESDAY

25

thursday | 57

Eileen - 1:39- 1:54

26

new moon

friday | 58

27

saturday | 59

28

sunday | 60

NOTES

1

MARCH

61 | monday
2

62 | tuesday
3

63 | wednesday
4

64 | thursday
first quarter 5

65 | friday
6

66 | saturday
7

S	M	T	W	T	F	S	MAR
1	2	3	4	5	6	7	
8	9	10	11	12	13	14	
15	16	17	18	19	20	21	
22	23	24	25	26	27	28	
29	30	31					

67 | sunday
8

MARCH

monday | 68

9

tuesday | 69

10

wednesday | 70

11

thursday | 71

12

friday | 72

13 *full moon*

saturday | 73

14

sunday | 74 | *NOTES*

15

Spring Break

75 | m o n d a y
16

ST. PATRICK'S DAY

76 | t u e s d a y
17

77 | w e d n e s d a y
18

78 | t h u r s d a y
19

79 | f r i d a y

vernal equinox
7:55 p.m. (GMT) **20**

80 | s a t u r d a y

last quarter **21**

S	M	T	W	T	F	S	MAR
1	2	3	4	5	6	7	
8	9	10	11	12	13	14	
15	16	17	18	19	20	21	
22	23	24	25	26	27	28	
29	30	31					

81 | s u n d a y
22

G is for GEORGE smothered under a rug

H is for HECTOR done in by a thug

MARCH

monday | 82
23

tuesday | 83
24

wednesday | 84
25

thursday | 85
26

friday | 86
27

saturday | 87
28   *new moon*

sunday | 88   *NOTES*
29

89 | monday

30

90 | tuesday

31

91 | wednesday

1

92 | thursday

2

93 | friday

first quarter

3

94 | saturday

4

S	M	T	W	T	F	S
			1	2	3	4
5	6	7	8	9	10	11
12	13	14	15	16	17	18
19	20	21	22	23	24	25
26	27	28	29	30		

APR

PALM SUNDAY

95 | sunday

5

APRIL

monday | 96

6

tuesday | 97

7

wednesday | 98

8

thursday | 99

9

friday | 100

10

GOOD FRIDAY
PASSOVER (begins at sundown)

saturday | 101

11 *full moon*

sunday | 102

12

EASTER SUNDAY

NOTES

EASTER MONDAY (Canada) 103 | m o n d a y

13

104 | t u e s d a y

14

105 | w e d n e s d a y

15

106 | t h u r s d a y

16

107 | f r i d a y

17

108 | s a t u r d a y

18

S	M	T	W	T	F	S	APR
			1	2	3	4	
5	6	7	8	9	10	11	
12	13	14	15	16	17	18	
19	20	21	22	23	24	25	
26	27	28	29	30			

109 | s u n d a y

last quarter

19

I is for IDA who drowned in a lake

J is for JAMES who took lye by mistake

APRIL

monday | 110

20

tuesday | 111

21

wednesday | 112   EARTH DAY

22

thursday | 113

23

friday | 114

24

saturday | 115

25

sunday | 116   *NOTES*

26   *new moon*

117 | monday

27

118 | tuesday

28

119 | wednesday

29

120 | thursday

30

121 | friday

1

122 | saturday

2

S	M	T	W	T	F	S
					1	2
3	4	5	6	7	8	9
10	11	12	13	14	15	16
17	18	19	20	21	22	23
24	25	26	27	28	29	30
31						

MAY

123 | sunday

first quarter **3**

MAY

monday | 124

4

tuesday | 125   CINCO DE MAYO

5

wednesday | 126

6

thursday | 127

7

friday | 128

8

saturday | 129

9

sunday | 130   MOTHER'S DAY | *NOTES*

10

131 | m o n d a y
full moon **11**

132 | t u e s d a y
12

133 | w e d n e s d a y
13

134 | t h u r s d a y
14

135 | f r i d a y
15

ARMED FORCES DAY

136 | s a t u r d a y
16

S	M	T	W	T	F	S	**MAY**
					1	2	
3	4	5	6	7	8	9	
10	11	12	13	14	15	16	
17	18	19	20	21	22	23	
24	25	26	27	28	29	30	
31							

137 | s u n d a y
17

K is for KATE who was struck with an axe

L is for LEO who swallowed some tacks

MAY

monday | 138
18

tuesday | 139
19   *last quarter*

wednesday | 140
20

thursday | 141
21

friday | 142
22

saturday | 143
23

sunday | 144   *NOTES*
24

MEMORIAL DAY (Observed)

145 | m o n d a y

new moon **25**

146 | t u e s d a y

26

147 | w e d n e s d a y

27

148 | t h u r s d a y

28

149 | f r i d a y

29

MEMORIAL DAY

150 | s a t u r d a y

30

S	M	T	W	T	F	S	MAY
					1	2	
3	4	5	6	7	8	9	
10	11	12	13	14	15	16	
17	18	19	20	21	22	23	
24	25	26	27	28	29	30	
31							

151 | s u n d a y

31

JUNE

monday | 152

1

tuesday | 153

2   *first quarter*

wednesday | 154

3

thursday | 155

4

friday | 156

5

saturday | 157

6

sunday | 158 | *NOTES*

7

159 | monday

8

160 | tuesday

9

Dr. Rosenberg   8:15 AM

161 | wednesday

full moon **10**

162 | thursday

11

June Music
4

163 | friday

12

164 | saturday

13

S	M	T	W	T	F	S
		1	2	3	4	5	6
7	8	9	10	11	12	13
14	15	16	17	18	19	20
21	22	23	24	25	26	27
28	29	30				

JUN | FLAG DAY

165 | sunday

June 4 am

14

M is for MAUD who was swept out to sea

N is for NEVILLE who died of ennui

JUNE

monday | 166

15

tuesday | 167

16

wednesday | 168

17 *last quarter*

thursday | 169

18

friday | 170

19

saturday | 171

20

sunday | 172   FATHER'S DAY | *NOTES*

21 *summer solstice*
2:03 p.m. (GMT)

	173	monday
Dr. Hume 2 pm		**22**

	174	tuesday
		23

	175	wednesday
new moon		**24**

	176	thursday
		25

	177	friday
		26

	178	saturday
		27

	179	sunday
		28

S	M	T	W	T	F	S	JUN
	1	2	3	4	5	6	
7	8	9	10	11	12	13	
14	15	16	17	18	19	20	
21	22	23	24	25	26	27	
28	29	30					

JUNE/JULY

monday | 180
29

tuesday | 181
30

wednesday | 182   CANADA DAY (Canada)
1
first quarter

thursday | 183
2

friday | 184
3

saturday | 185   INDEPENDENCE DAY
4

sunday | 186   *NOTES*
5

187 | monday

6

188 | tuesday

7

189 | wednesday

8

190 | thursday

full moon **9**

191 | friday

10

192 | saturday

11

S	M	T	W	T	F	S	JUL
			1	2	3	4	
5	6	7	8	9	10	11	
12	13	14	15	16	17	18	
19	20	21	22	23	24	25	
26	27	28	29	30	31		

193 | sunday

12

O is for OLIVE run through with an awl

P is for PRUE trampled flat in a brawl

monday | 194

13

tuesday | 195

14

wednesday | 196

15

thursday | 197

16 *last quarter*

friday | 198

17

saturday | 199

18

sunday | 200 | *NOTES*

19

201 | monday
20

202 | tuesday
21

203 | wednesday
22

204 | thursday
new moon **23**

205 | friday
24

206 | saturday
25

S	M	T	W	T	F	S	JUL
			1	2	3	4	
5	6	7	8	9	10	11	
12	13	14	15	16	17	18	
19	20	21	22	23	24	25	
26	27	28	29	30	31		

207 | sunday
26

monday | 208

27

tuesday | 209

28

wednesday | 210

29

thursday | 211

30

friday | 212

31 *first quarter*

saturday | 213

1

sunday | 214 | *NOTES*

2

215 | monday

3

216 | tuesday

4

217 | wednesday

5

218 | thursday

6

219 | friday

7

220 | saturday

full moon

8

S	M	T	W	T	F	S	AUG
						1	
2	3	4	5	6	7	8	
9	10	11	12	13	14	15	
16	17	18	19	20	21	22	
23	24	25	26	27	28	29	
30	31						

221 | sunday

9

Q is for QUENTIN who sank in a mire

R is for RHODA consumed by a fire

AUGUST

monday | 222
10

tuesday | 223
11

wednesday | 224
12

thursday | 225
13

friday | 226
14
last quarter

saturday | 227
15

sunday | 228
16

NOTES

229 | monday

17

230 | tuesday

18

231 | wednesday

19

232 | thursday

20

233 | friday

21

234 | saturday

new moon

22

S	M	T	W	T	F	S		AUG
						1		
2	3	4	5	6	7	8		
9	10	11	12	13	14	15		
16	17	18	19	20	21	22		
23	24	25	26	27	28	29		
30	31							

235 | sunday

23

AUGUST

monday | 236
24

tuesday | 237
25

wednesday | 238
26

thursday | 239
27

friday | 240
28

saturday | 241
29

sunday | 242
30
first quarter

NOTES

243 | monday
31

244 | tuesday
1

245 | wednesday
2

246 | thursday
3

247 | friday
4

248 | saturday
5

S	M	T	W	T	F	S	**SEP**
		1	2	3	4	5	
6	7	8	9	10	11	12	
13	14	15	16	17	18	19	
20	21	22	23	24	25	26	
27	28	29	30				

249 | sunday

full moon **6**

S is for SUSAN who perished of fits

T is for TITUS who flew into bits

SEPTEMBER

monday | 250   LABOR DAY (U.S. & Canada)

7

tuesday | 251

8

wednesday | 252

9

thursday | 253

10

friday | 254

11

saturday | 255

12

sunday | 256   *NOTES*

13
last quarter

257 | monday
14

258 | tuesday
15

259 | wednesday
16

260 | thursday
17

261 | friday
18

262 | saturday
19

S	M	T	W	T	F	S
		1	2	3	4	5
6	7	8	9	10	11	12
13	14	15	16	17	18	19
20	21	22	23	24	25	26
27	28	29	30			

ROSH HASHANAH
(begins at sundown)

263 | sunday

new moon
20

SEPTEMBER

monday | 264
21

tuesday | 265
22

wednesday | 266
23
autumnal equinox
5:37 a.m. (GMT)

thursday | 267
24

friday | 268
25

saturday | 269
26

sunday | 270
27

NOTES

271 | m o n d a y

first quarter **28**

272 | t u e s d a y

YOM KIPPUR (begins at sundown)

29

273 | w e d n e s d a y

30

274 | t h u r s d a y

1

275 | f r i d a y

2

276 | s a t u r d a y

3

OCT	S	M	T	W	T	F	S
					1	2	3
	4	5	6	7	8	9	10
	11	12	13	14	15	16	17
	18	19	20	21	22	23	24
	25	26	27	28	29	30	31

277 | s u n d a y

4

U is for UNA who slipped down a drain

V is for VICTOR squashed under a train

OCTOBER

monday | 278

5 *full moon*

tuesday | 279

6

wednesday | 280

7

thursday | 281

8

friday | 282

9

saturday | 283

10

sunday | 284

11 *Irish Birthday*

NOTES

COLUMBUS DAY
THANKSGIVING DAY (Canada)

285 | monday

last quarter

12

286 | tuesday

13

287 | wednesday

14

288 | thursday

15

289 | friday

16

290 | saturday

17

S	M	T	W	T	F	S	OCT
				1	2	3	
4	5	6	7	8	9	10	
11	12	13	14	15	16	17	
18	19	20	21	22	23	24	
25	26	27	28	29	30	31	

291 | sunday

18

OCTOBER

monday | 292
19

tuesday | 293
20 *new moon*

wednesday | 294
21

thursday | 295
22

friday | 296
23

saturday | 297   UNITED NATIONS DAY
24

sunday | 298   *NOTES*
25

299 | monday

26

300 | tuesday

27

301 | wednesday

first quarter **28**

anni?

302 | thursday

29

303 | friday

30

HALLOWEEN

304 | saturday

31

S	M	T	W	T	F	S	NOV
1	2	3	4	5	6	7	
8	9	10	11	12	13	14	
15	16	17	18	19	20	21	
22	23	24	25	26	27	28	
29	30						

305 | sunday

1

W is for WINNIE embedded in ice

X is for XERXES devoured by mice

NOVEMBER

monday | 306

2

tuesday | 307   ELECTION DAY

3

wednesday | 308

4   *full moon*

thursday | 309

5

friday | 310

6

saturday | 311

7

sunday | 312 | *NOTES*

8

313 | monday

9

314 | tuesday

10

VETERANS DAY
REMEMBRANCE DAY (Canada)

315 | wednesday

last quarter

11

316 | thursday

12

317 | friday

13

318 | saturday

14

S	M	T	W	T	F	S	NOV
1	2	3	4	5	6	7	
8	9	10	11	12	13	14	
15	16	17	18	19	20	21	
22	23	24	25	26	27	28	
29	30						

319 | sunday

15

NOVEMBER

monday | 320
16

tuesday | 321
17

wednesday | 322
18

thursday | 323
19   *new moon*

friday | 324
20

saturday | 325
21

sunday | 326   *NOTES*
22

327 | m o n d a y
23

328 | t u e s d a y
24

329 | w e d n e s d a y
25

THANKSGIVING DAY   330 | t h u r s d a y
26

331 | f r i d a y

first quarter   ## 27

332 | s a t u r d a y
28

S	M	T	W	T	F	S	NOV
1	2	3	4	5	6	7	
8	9	10	11	12	13	14	
15	16	17	18	19	20	21	
22	23	24	25	26	27	28	
29	30						

333 | s u n d a y
29

Y is for YORICK whose head was knocked in

Z is for ZILLAH who drank too much gin

NOVEMBER/DECEMBER

monday | 334

30

tuesday | 335

1

wednesday | 336

2

thursday | 337

3   *full moon*

friday | 338

4

saturday | 339

5

sunday | 340   *NOTES*

6

341 | monday

7

342 | tuesday

8

343 | wednesday

9

344 | thursday

last quarter **10**

345 | friday

11

346 | saturday

12

S	M	T	W	T	F	S
		1	2	3	4	5
6	7	8	9	10	11	12
13	14	15	16	17	18	19
20	21	22	23	24	25	26
27	28	29	30	31		

DEC | HANUKKAH (begins at sundown)   347 | sunday

13

DECEMBER

monday | 348

14

tuesday | 349

15

wednesday | 350

16

thursday | 351

17

friday | 352

18   *new moon*

saturday | 353

19

sunday | 354 | *NOTES*

20

355 | monday

21

356 | tuesday

winter solstice
1:56 a.m. (GMT)

22

357 | wednesday

23

358 | thursday

24

CHRISTMAS DAY

359 | friday

25

BOXING DAY (Canada)

360 | saturday

first quarter

26

S	M	T	W	T	F	S	DEC
		1	2	3	4	5	
6	7	8	9	10	11	12	
13	14	15	16	17	18	19	
20	21	22	23	24	25	26	
27	28	29	30	31			

361 | sunday

27

DECEMBER/JANUARY

monday | 362

28

tuesday | 363

29

wednesday | 364

30

thursday | 365

31

friday | 1   NEW YEAR'S DAY

1

saturday | 2

2 *full moon*

sunday | 3 | *NOTES*

3

Name _____

Address _____

City _____

State _____

Zip _____

Phone _____

Fax _____

E-mail _____

In case of emergency, please notify:

Name *Charles Groffman*

Address *PO Box 6332   87197 / 3528 12th nw*

City *Albuq.*   *87104*

State *N.M.*

Zip _____

Phone *344 2657*

Medical Information:

Physician's name *Dr. Papafrangos*

Physician's phone *462-2600*

Health insurance company *Presbyterian*

Plan number _____

Allergies _____

Other _____

Other Information:

Driver's license number _____

Car insurance company *~~the~~ Hartford*

Policy number _____

1998 year at a glance

JANUARY

S	M	T	W	T	F	S
				1	2	3
4	5	6	7	8	9	10
11	12	13	14	15	16	17
18	19	20	21	22	23	24
25	26	27	28	29	30	31

FEBRUARY

S	M	T	W	T	F	S
1	2	3	4	5	6	7
8	9	10	11	12	13	14
15	16	17	18	19	20	21
22	23	24	25	26	27	28

MARCH

S	M	T	W	T	F	S
1	2	3	4	5	6	7
8	9	10	11	12	13	14
15	16	17	18	19	20	21
22	23	24	25	26	27	28
29	30	31				

APRIL

S	M	T	W	T	F	S
			1	2	3	4
5	6	7	8	9	10	11
12	13	14	15	16	17	18
19	20	21	22	23	24	25
26	27	28	29	30		

MAY

S	M	T	W	T	F	S
					1	2
3	4	5	6	7	8	9
10	11	12	13	14	15	16
17	18	19	20	21	22	23
24	25	26	27	28	29	30
31						

JUNE

S	M	T	W	T	F	S
	1	2	3	4	5	6
7	8	9	10	11	12	13
14	15	16	17	18	19	20
21	22	23	24	25	26	27
28	29	30				

JULY

S	M	T	W	T	F	S
			1	2	3	4
5	6	7	8	9	10	11
12	13	14	15	16	17	18
19	20	21	22	23	24	25
26	27	28	29	30	31	

AUGUST

S	M	T	W	T	F	S
						1
2	3	4	5	6	7	8
9	10	11	12	13	14	15
16	17	18	19	20	21	22
23	24	25	26	27	28	29
30	31					

SEPTEMBER

S	M	T	W	T	F	S
		1	2	3	4	5
6	7	8	9	10	11	12
13	14	15	16	17	18	19
20	21	22	23	24	25	26
27	28	29	30			

OCTOBER

S	M	T	W	T	F	S
				1	2	3
4	5	6	7	8	9	10
11	12	13	14	15	16	17
18	19	20	21	22	23	24
25	26	27	28	29	30	31

NOVEMBER

S	M	T	W	T	F	S
1	2	3	4	5	6	7
8	9	10	11	12	13	14
15	16	17	18	19	20	21
22	23	24	25	26	27	28
29	30					

DECEMBER

S	M	T	W	T	F	S
		1	2	3	4	5
6	7	8	9	10	11	12
13	14	15	16	17	18	19
20	21	22	23	24	25	26
27	28	29	30	31		

JANUARY

S	M	T	W	T	F	S
					1	2
3	4	5	6	7	8	9
10	11	12	13	14	15	16
17	18	19	20	21	22	23
24	25	26	27	28	29	30
31						

MAY

S	M	T	W	T	F	S
						1
2	3	4	5	6	7	8
9	10	11	12	13	14	15
16	17	18	19	20	21	22
23	24	25	26	27	28	29
30	31					

SEPTEMBER

S	M	T	W	T	F	S
			1	2	3	4
5	6	7	8	9	10	11
12	13	14	15	16	17	18
19	20	21	22	23	24	25
26	27	28	29	30		

FEBRUARY

S	M	T	W	T	F	S
	1	2	3	4	5	6
7	8	9	10	11	12	13
14	15	16	17	18	19	20
21	22	23	24	25	26	27
28						

JUNE

S	M	T	W	T	F	S
		1	2	3	4	5
6	7	8	9	10	11	12
13	14	15	16	17	18	19
20	21	22	23	24	25	26
27	28	29	30			

OCTOBER

S	M	T	W	T	F	S
					1	2
3	4	5	6	7	8	9
10	11	12	13	14	15	16
17	18	19	20	21	22	23
24	25	26	27	28	29	30
31						

MARCH

S	M	T	W	T	F	S
	1	2	3	4	5	6
7	8	9	10	11	12	13
14	15	16	17	18	19	20
21	22	23	24	25	26	27
28	29	30	31			

JULY

S	M	T	W	T	F	S
				1	2	3
4	5	6	7	8	9	10
11	12	13	14	15	16	17
18	19	20	21	22	23	24
25	26	27	28	29	30	31

NOVEMBER

S	M	T	W	T	F	S
	1	2	3	4	5	6
7	8	9	10	11	12	13
14	15	16	17	18	19	20
21	22	23	24	25	26	27
28	29	30				

APRIL

S	M	T	W	T	F	S
				1	2	3
4	5	6	7	8	9	10
11	12	13	14	15	16	17
18	19	20	21	22	23	24
25	26	27	28	29	30	

AUGUST

S	M	T	W	T	F	S
1	2	3	4	5	6	7
8	9	10	11	12	13	14
15	16	17	18	19	20	21
22	23	24	25	26	27	28
29	30	31				

DECEMBER

S	M	T	W	T	F	S
			1	2	3	4
5	6	7	8	9	10	11
12	13	14	15	16	17	18
19	20	21	22	23	24	25
26	27	28	29	30	31	

notes

notes

Margaret Rider
   643 Mapleton Ave.
      Boulder, CO 80304

Anne - Oct. 28 (77)
Trish - Oct. 11
Eileen - Oct. 21 (43)
Grace - June 29   76 in 99
Sandy H. - Feb. 10
Bill - May 31
Chuck - Jan. 15
James - Dec. 18   12/18/68
Natalie - May 31
Allison - Dec. 31
Michael 5/7

Marin - July 4